Tweety Investigates
STICKER
SCENE STORY

PARR 10268

Bath New York Singapore Hong Kong Cologne Delhi Melbourne

The Posh Society Ball was one of the biggest events of the year and Granny, Sylvester, and Tweety were looking their best. Inside the ballroom, the richest people in town were all there to celebrate the event,

The evening was guaranteed to be more exciting than they could have imagined!

Granny was invited to the party because her grandfather, Percival Posh, was the society's founder. His portrait hung near the entrance to the ballroom.

"That's Grandpa Percy," she said to her pets as they passed it. "He was once the richest man in town, but lost every penny by the time I was born."

PERCIVAL POSH
FOUNDER OF OUR SOCIETY

Warren Van Cash, the society's president, greeted Granny. But soon, he was distracted by all the guests showing off their pricey jewels to one another and left the room.

"Look at my million dollar bracelet," said one.

"My necklace is worth five million dollars," said another.

And that was when it happened!

"I've been robbed," Mrs. Moolah shrieked. "My million dollar necklace is gone!"

"And so is mine!" "And mine!" "And mine too!"

These cries echoed throughout the ballroom. Soon, all the guests were in uproar as everyone reached for their cell phones to report the great jewel robbery to the police.

Sylvester saw his chance to finally catch Tweety.
"With all this chaos, who's going to notice me?" he thought.
Tweety saw the look in his eyes and dashed off quickly.
Sylvester knocked over a platter of food, spilled two bowls of
punch, and jumped on all eighty-eight keys of the piano in
his pursuit of the fleeing Tweety.

Tweety ran through people's legs, under tables, and over empty chairs. But Sylvester didn't give up that easily. Tweety had to make sure he stayed away from the naughty puddy tat's claws, so he flew up and hid among the crystals of the gigantic chandelier above the ballroom.

"I should be safe up here," Tweety thought.

From this view, Tweety could see the whole room and everyone in it. Among all the beautiful guests, Tweety's eye was caught by a heavy woman in a lavish blue gown. She walked past the huge portrait of Granny's grandfather, Percival Posh, and poked her hand behind the frame.

"Whatever is that woman doing?" Tweety asked himself.

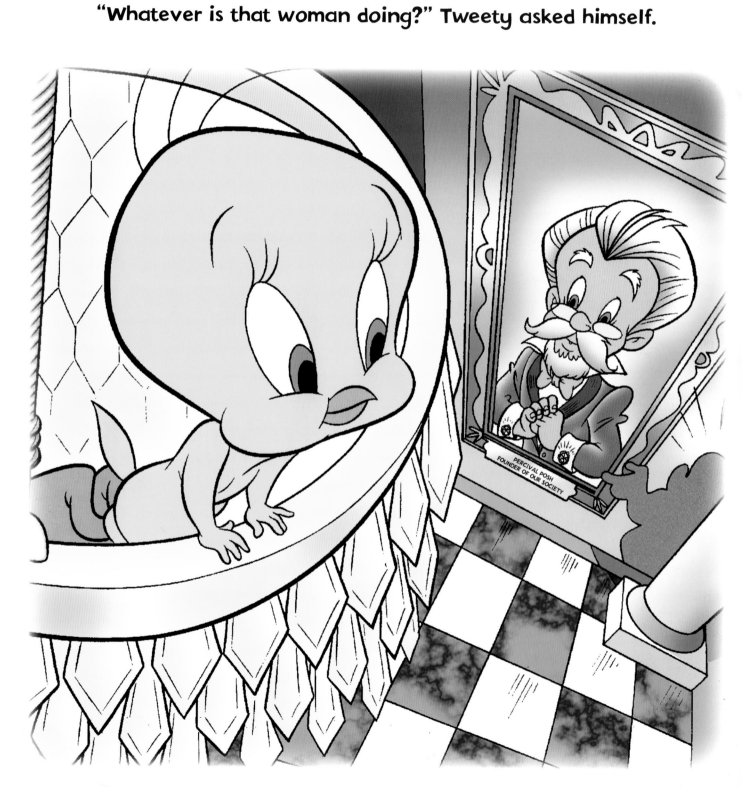

PERCIVAL POSH
NDER OF OUR SOCIETY

Tweety watched the woman in the blue dress. She walked back and forth, going from a bejewelled woman on the ballroom floor to the portrait of Percival Posh. Then she'd start all over again. Each time this happened, a guest would call out that she had been robbed. Luckily, Granny's favorite five dollar ring wasn't valuable enough to be taken!

Tweety had been so busy trying to escape from Sylvester that he had forgotten all about the robbery.

"Could she be the wobber?" Tweety asked himself. The canary then wondered how he could possibly stop her and still keep himself safe from Sylvester.

"But I've got to do something," he decided. So he did!

PERCIVAL POSH
FOUNDER OF OUR SOCIETY

Tweety quickly flew down from the chandelier and moved toward Percival Posh's portrait. Spotting him, Sylvester's eyes lit up and he headed for Tweety.

"I'm going to get you!" he exclaimed, as he ran full speed toward the portrait.

"I hope I know what I'm doing," thought Tweety.

PERCIVAL POSH
FOUNDER OF OUR SOCIETY

The woman in the blue dress walked toward the portrait. Tweety flew by and landed on the picture frame. Sylvester leaped toward Tweety and the portrait.

"Oh, no" the woman cried, in a deep, loud voice.

But it was too late. **CRASH! SLAM! BANG!** Sylvester smashed straight into the large portrait.

"Look!" screamed a huge group of people.

Sylvester had unloosened a treasure trove of jewelry that had been hidden behind the portrait when he crashed into it.

The woman in the blue dress knelt down, trying to scoop up as many of the stolen jewels as she could. But it was game over!

It was **Warren Van Cash**, the society's president. He had dressed up as a woman to commit the robberies.

"I'd lost everything," he blurted out. "I had to get it back."

"Percival Posh lost everything too," said Granny, "but he always remained decent and honest, and the proud founder of this society! You should be ashamed of yourself."

Granny was very proud of the part her two pets played in helping the guests recover their missing jewelry.

"You two really solved the mystery," said Granny, kissing Tweety and patting Sylvester. "You're quite a good team when you work together."

"Oh brother," Tweety muttered. "That will never happen!"